AVE MARIA

Text: Luke 1
Music: Franz Schubert (1797 - 1828)

na,
bis,

Ma - ri - a gra-ti-a ple - na,
o - ra, o - ra pro no - bis

Do-mi-nus te-
pec-ca-to - ri-

cum,
bus,

be - ne - di - cta tu in mu-li-e - ri-bus,
nunc et in ho-ra mor-tis no - strae,

et
in

be - ne - di - ctus,
ho - ra mor - tis no - strae,

et be - ne - di - ctus fru - ctus
nunc et in ho-ra mor - tis

ven - tris,
no - strae,

ven - tris tu - i, Je - sus.
in ho - ra mor - tis no - strae.

A - ve Ma - ri - a!
A - ve Ma - ri - a!

dim. al fine

AVE MARIA

Text: Luke 1
Music: adapted from J. S. Bach
by Charles Gounod (1818 - 1893)

gra - ti - a ple - na, Do - mi - nus

te - cum, be - ne - di - cta

tu in mu - li - e - ri - bus,

et be - ne - di - ctus fru - ctus

ven - tris tu - i Je - sus.

cresc. poco a poco

San - cta Ma - ri - a, san - cta Ma-

ri - a, Ma - ri - a! O - ra pro

no - bis, no - bis pec - ca - to - ri - bus

nunc et in ho - ra, in ho - ra

mor - tis no - strae, A - men,

A - men.

We hope you enjoy the music in this book.
Further copies of this are available from your local
music shop or Christian bookshop.

In case of difficulty, please contact the publisher direct:

The Sales Department
KEVIN MAYHEW LTD
Rattlesden
Bury St Edmunds
Suffolk IP30 0SZ

Phone 01449 737978
Fax 01449 737834

Please ask for our complete catalogue of outstanding Church Music.

Front Cover: *Madonna and Child with Angels.* Flemish school (16th Century).
Reproduced by courtesy of Rafael Valls Gallery, London

Cover designed by Graham Johnstone and Veronica Ward

First published in Great Britain in 1994 by Kevin Mayhew Ltd

This compilation © Copyright 1996 Kevin Mayhew Ltd

ISBN 0 86209 782 7
Catalogue No: 1450040

All or part of these pieces have been arranged by Anthea Smith
and are the copyright of Kevin Mayhew Ltd.

Music Editor: Anthea Smith
Music Setting: Tricia Oliver

Printed and bound in Great Britain